Self-help helps it work even better

Classic cognitive behaviour therapy (CBT) works well for people with mild to moderate depression and anxiety, but it's a scarce resource, demanding a lot of practitioner time.

CBT self-help uses less practitioner time and can often reach more people. And they like it. You only have to look at the growing self-help sections in bookshops to know how popular it is.

One reason is the way it empowers individuals to make changes when and where they want, at a pace that suits. The patient/client is in charge of his or her therapy.

It's flexible – people can do as much or as little as they wish, working on problems that are relevant at the moment.

And resources come in different shapes and sizes, like people. Large, detailed books suit some and easier, more accessible approaches suit others.

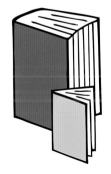

In every case, however, the practitioner's role is different to that in classic CBT…

WITH SELF-HELP, YOU'RE A COACH, NOT A THERAPIST

Self-help means just that – people help themselves.

The support materials do a lot of the work, so you don't have to deliver the psychotherapy or counselling. Instead, your role is Supportive Monitoring.

You encourage people to use and get the most from the self-help materials and you monitor their progress as they learn new skills and try them out.

When you meet or speak on the phone, you're still involved in talking therapy, but it's talking that's focused on the materials - helping people to understand them and how to get the most from them.

Your patient chooses the issue to work on and how he or she wants to work. What you provide is friendly encouragement.

WHY DO I FEEL SO BAD?

I'M NOT GOOD ENOUGH

SO.
HOW DO
YOU USE
THE LITTLE
BOOKS?

There are six steps

Your job is to collaborate with your patient in deciding on the problem, choosing the book and setting off on the self-help journey.

He or she does this by working through the book and following its instructions and suggestions.

Your role is to monitor progress, help overcome obstacles and review the project as a whole.

In all, there are 6 steps to the practitioner's side of the CBT self-help process and they're explained on the next few pages.

READ 'EM TILL THE COVERS COME OFF

Get to know the books backwards

You must know the books well and believe in them before you can assess whether they are right for a particular patient, and which one you might use in what circumstances.

Bear in mind that your patient will spend more time with the books than with you, and will want to discuss ideas and actions that are mentioned in them.
It's embarrassing being asked a question about the content and not being familiar with it, so you'll need to be aware of the language and imagery.

The patient may mention things like the E4SP or the ABTBP and might even go on about eating an elephant. You'll need to be able to respond!

A caveat: if you're not so convinced by self-help or the books, your patient will sense your doubts and may not be wholehearted about this way of working. It might be better to look at other low intensity alternatives like groups, behavioural activation and case management.

E4SP
ABTBP

STEP 2

ASK: DO YOU WANT TO TRY SELF-HELP?

It doesn't work for everyone

The success rate among people who don't want to work this way is low, so assess your patient's reaction to the idea of self-help.

"Have you used self-help materials before? Did they work? What do your family and friends think about this approach?"

You'll need to describe and discuss the process and work out whether there are any practical issues that might affect the person's ability to work this way.

Poor eyesight or reading? The little books are very accessible, but if even they seem daunting, suggest DVD or audio versions.

Too depressed? Low concentration or agitation? It may not be the right time for self-help. Other treatments may be needed first.

And bear risk in mind. If you think there's serious depression or an active risk of suicide, do a full mental health assessment or refer the patient for this.

Make the point that self-help is active – it's all about learning new skills that help you cope with feelings, life and problems.

Don't proceed unless you get active agreement to 'give it a try'.

DO A
5-AREAS
ASSESSMENT

The 5 Areas approach says that the way we feel affects five key aspects of our lives.

When we feel low or distressed we can notice altered thinking, altered feelings or altered physical symptoms. These alter our behaviour and activity levels and a vicious circle starts spinning down and down.

But by changing just one thing (situations, feelings, thinking, behaviours or physical symptoms) the others will also improve – the vicious circle starts to unwind and things get better.

Identify a problem to work on

Using *'Why do I feel so bad?'* work through the 5-Areas concept. Now identify one problem and choose the area to work on. Do this together. Remember, you only need to fix one thing and the others will follow.

For practical problems (need a job, need to stop spending, using, cutting etc) *'How to fix almost everything'* is a good choice.

People with negative thought patterns may choose to work on *'Why does everything always go wrong?'*

People who drink too much or respond in other ways that backfire might choose *'The things you do that mess you up'*

And people with low motivation and mood could choose *'I can't be bothered doing anything'* to work with.

There are other books too, covering more specific issues such as anger, low self-esteem, healthy living, suicidal ideas etc (see inside back cover) and more are added all the time.

I CAN'T BE BOTHERED DOING ANYTHING

STEP 4

EXPLAIN HOW TO USE THE CHOSEN BOOK

It's a work book, not just a reading book

Self-help always involves making a positive plan for change - actions **are** required.

Make this clear to your patient and go through the key headings of the selected book (you know it well, of course), explaining how to set aside time for daily sessions and where plans, decisions, notes and other work will be needed.

Be positive but realistic. Don't gloss over possible problems along the way, but make it clear that many, many people have changed their lives for the better with self-help CBT.

At this stage, you might also wish to hand over the companion book *'Write all over your bathroom mirror'*. This "how to" book for patients encourages action and ownership and has tips on how to get the most from this way of working.

WRITE ALL OVER YOUR BATHROOM MIRROR

ASK:
HOW WOULD
YOU LIKE
TO BE
SUPPORTED?

Let the person decide

Before the initial session is over, agree with the patient how much and how often you'll stay in touch from now on.

Depending on resources, you could offer further face-to-face sessions, phone support (for set periods at pre-arranged times), email contact or live online chat by appointment. Offer what fits your patient and fits the resources you have to offer. The key is to engage the person.

Most people can do well with 3-4 short support contacts of 10-20 minutes or so – however this will vary with the patient and the aims of the service.

Remember to use words and examples that engage and work for the person you are supporting. Avoid jargon and make things relevant.

REVIEW AND RE-ENERGISE AT SUPPORT SESSIONS

Remember, you're a coach

You provide encouragement and practical support.

Help your patient to get specific. Rather than thinking "I'll do it this week sometime" help him or her to plan what to do, when to do it and what might block the plan.

Point out the planning pages in their chosen booklet and encourage use of the agenda slips at the back of *'Write all over your bathroom mirror'* to prepare for meetings with you.

If the patient is succeeding, use praise and reinforcement to maintain progress. If not, suggest unblockers (refer to *'Write all over your bathroom mirror'* or use the techniques in *'How to fix almost anything'*).

If difficulties persist, suggest a re-setting of goals or a change of plan to make it easier to achieve. Some people may need to drop self-help and switch to a different approach.

Your patient needs to know what to do and say if they feel things aren't going well. It's no-one's failure, but another approach may be needed.

Throughout, be yourself, be positive, be realistic.

Support session plan overleaf

THINGS TO COVER IN A FIRST SUPPORT SESSION

The self-help approach

- "Have you used any self-help books before? Did they help?"

- We are offering supported self-help that uses written booklets for you to use at home, and with support from me to help you keep on track."

The aim of self-help

- "It helps you understand why you feel as you do."

- "You'll learn new ways of coping with your problems."

- "Skills and workbooks can be used again in future. It's your own personal resource pack."

What you will learn

- "It's a practical approach –you'll learn techniques and tools that will help you turn the corner to recovery."

- "It's all based on Cognitive Behaviour Therapy - a way of helping with depression and anxiety that has really worked for lots of people."